WITHDRAWN

PLEASE WASH
YOUR HANDS
BEFORE YOU READ ME
AND KEEP ME CLEAN

WENDY WATSON'S
MOTHER
GOOSE

WENDY WATSON'S

MOTHER
GOOSE

Lothrop, Lee & Shepard Books
New York

Illustrations copyright © 1989 by Wendy Watson
All rights reserved. No part of this book may be reproduced or utilized in any form or by
any means, electronic or mechanical, including photocopying, recording or by any
information storage and retrieval system, without permission in writing from the
Publisher. Inquiries should be addressed to Lothrop, Lee & Shepard Books, a division of
William Morrow & Company, Inc., 105 Madison Avenue, New York, New York 10016.

First Edition 1 2 3 4 5 6 7 8 9 10

Library of Congress Cataloging in Publication Data
Mother Goose. Wendy Watson's Mother Goose.
p.   cm.   Includes indexes. Summary: An illustrated collection of the
traditional rhymes. ISBN 0-688-05708-X. 1. Nursery rhymes. 2. Children's poetry.
[1. Nursery rhymes.] I. Watson, Wendy, ill. II. Title. PZ8.3.M85
1989f 398'.8—dc19 88-37913 CIP AC
Printed in Singapore.

If you are not handsome at twenty
Not strong at thirty
Not rich at forty
Not wise at fifty,
You never will be.

Donkey, donkey, old and gray,
Open your mouth and gently bray.
Lift your ears and blow your horn
To wake the world this sleepy morn.

Lock the dairy door! Lock the dairy door!
Chickle chackle chee, I haven't got the key!

Friday night's dream
On Saturday told
Is sure to come true,
Be it ever so old.

He that would thrive
Must rise at five.
He that hath thriven
May lie till seven.
He that will never thrive
May lie till eleven.

Pussycat, pussycat, where have you been?
I've been to London to visit the queen.
Pussycat, pussycat, what did you there?
I frightened a little mouse under her chair.

Here we go round the mulberry bush,
The mulberry bush, the mulberry bush.
Here we go round the mulberry bush
On a cold and frosty morning.

This is the way we wash our hands,
Wash our hands, wash our hands.
This is the way we wash our hands
On a cold and frosty morning.

This is the way we wash our clothes,
Wash our clothes, wash our clothes.
This is the way we wash our clothes
On a cold and frosty morning.

This is the way we go to school,
Go to school, go to school.
This is the way we go to school
On a cold and frosty morning.

This is the way we come out of school,
Come out of school, come out of school.
This is the way we come out of school
On a cold and frosty morning.

This little pig went to market
This little pig stayed home
This little pig had roast beef
This little pig had none
And this little pig cried, Wee wee wee,
All the way home.

Elsie Marley is grown so fine
She won't get up to feed the swine
But lies in bed till eight or nine,
Lazy Elsie Marley.

Barber, barber, shave a pig.
How many hairs to make a wig?
Four-and-twenty, that's enough.
Give the barber a pinch of snuff.

Hiccup, hiccup, go away,
Come again another day.
Hiccup, hiccup, when I bake
I'll give to you a butter cake.

Little Robin Redbreast
Sat upon a rail.
Niddle noddle went his head,
Wiggle waggle went his tail.

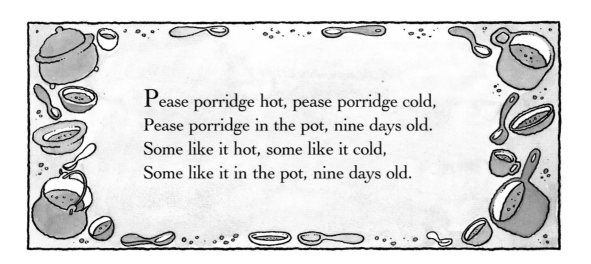

Pease porridge hot, pease porridge cold,
Pease porridge in the pot, nine days old.
Some like it hot, some like it cold,
Some like it in the pot, nine days old.

One, two, three four,
Mary at the cottage door.
Five, six, seven, eight,
Eating cherries off a plate.

Old Mother Hubbard
Went to the cupboard
To fetch her poor dog a bone,
But when she came there
The cupboard was bare,
And so the poor dog had none.

Monday's child is fair of face

Tuesday's child is full of grace

Wednesday's child is full of woe

Thursday's child has far to go

Friday's child is loving and giving

Saturday's child works hard for a living

And the child that is born on the Sabbath day

Is bonny and blithe and good and gay.

Charley Warley had a cow,
Black and white around the brow.
Open the gate and let her go through,
Charley Warley's old cow.

Jack and Jill
Went up the hill
To fetch a pail of water.
Jack fell down
And broke his crown,
And Jill came tumbling after.

Then up Jack got
And home did trot
As fast as he could caper.
He went to bed
And mended his head
With vinegar and brown paper.

Hickety pickety, my black hen,
She lays eggs for gentlemen.
Gentlemen come every day
To see what my black hen doth lay.
Sometimes nine and sometimes ten,
Hickety pickety, my black hen.

Once I saw a little bird
Come hop, hop, hop,
And I cried, Little bird,
Will you stop, stop, stop?

I was going to the window
To say how do you do,
But he shook his little tail
And away he flew.

See a pin and pick it up,
All the day you'll have good luck.
See a pin and let it lie,
Sure you'll want before you die.

One misty, moisty morning,
When cloudy was the weather,
I chanced to meet an old man
Clothed all in leather.
He began to compliment
And I began to grin.
How do you do, and how do you do,
And how do you do again?

Come, butter, come.
Come, butter, come.
Peter stands at the gate
Waiting for a butter cake.
Come, butter, come.

My learned friend and neighbor Pig —
Odds bobs and bills and dash my wig! —
'Tis said that you the weather know;
Please tell me when the wind will blow.

Blow, wind, blow! and go, mill, go!
That the miller may grind his corn,
That the baker may take it
And into bread make it
And bring us a loaf in the morn.

Patty cake, patty cake,
Baker's man,
Bake me a cake
As fast as you can.
Pat it and prick it
And mark it with B
And put it in the oven
For Baby and me.

Eat, birds, eat, and make no waste.
I lie here and make no haste.
If my master chance to come
You must fly and I must run.

Away you black devils, away.
Away you black devils, away.
You eat too much,
You drink too much,
You carry too much away.

We've ploughed our land,
We've sown our seed,
We've made all neat and gay,
So take a bit and leave a bit.
Away, birds, away!

One for the pigeon
One for the crow
One to rot
And one to grow.

Humpty Dumpty sat on a wall,
Humpty Dumpty had a great fall.
All the king's horses and all the king's men
Couldn't put Humpty together again.

I love little pussy,
Her coat is so warm,
And if I don't hurt her
She'll do me no harm.
So I'll not pull her tail
Nor drive her away,
But pussy and I
Very gently will play.

Little Tommy Tittlemouse
Lived in a little house.
He caught fishes
In other men's ditches.

Who are you? A dirty old man
I've always been since the day I began.
Mother and Father were dirty before me,
Hot or cold water has never come o'er me.

Ickle ockle, blue bockle,
Fishes in the sea,
If you want a pretty maid
Please choose me.

Good morrow to you, Valentine.
Curl your locks as I do mine,
Two before and three behind.
Good morrow to you, Valentine.

Then let us sing merrily, merrily now,
We'll live on the custards that come from the cow.

Red stockings, blue stockings,
Shoes tied up with silver,
A red rosette upon my breast
And a gold ring on my finger.

Birds of a feather flock together.
So do pigs and swine.
Rats and mice will have their choice
And so will I have mine.

I wrote a letter to my love
And on the way I dropped it.
A little puppy picked it up
And put it in his pocket.

One I love
Two I love
Three I love, I say,
Four I love with all my heart
Five I cast away.
Six he loves
Seven she loves
Eight they both love.
Nine he comes
Ten he tarries
Eleven he courts
Twelve he marries.

Pussycat, pussycat, wilt thou be mine?
Thou shalt neither wash dishes nor feed the swine,
But sit on a cushion and sew a silk seam
And eat fine strawberries, sugar, and cream.

Little Miss Muffet
Sat on a tuffet
Eating her curds and whey.
There came a big spider
Who sat down beside her
And frightened Miss Muffet away.

Young Roger came tapping at Dolly's window,
  Thumpaty thumpaty thump.
He begged for admittance, she answered him no,
  Glumpaty glumpaty glump.

My Dolly, my dear, your true love is here,
  Dumpaty dumpaty dump.
No, no, Roger, no, as you came you may go,
  Stumpaty stumpaty stump.

Sally, Sally Waters, sprinkle in the pan,
Hie Sally, hie Sally, for a young man.
    Choose for the best
    Choose for the worst
Choose for the prettiest that you like best.

There was an old crow
Sat upon a clod.
That's the end of my song —
That's odd.

P with a little o
S with a t
O double f
And i-c-e.

Ride a horse to Boston,
Ride a horse to Lynn.
Be careful of the rosebush —
You might fall in.

When land is gone and money spent
Then learning is most excellent.

I'm the king of the castle
And you're the dirty rascal.

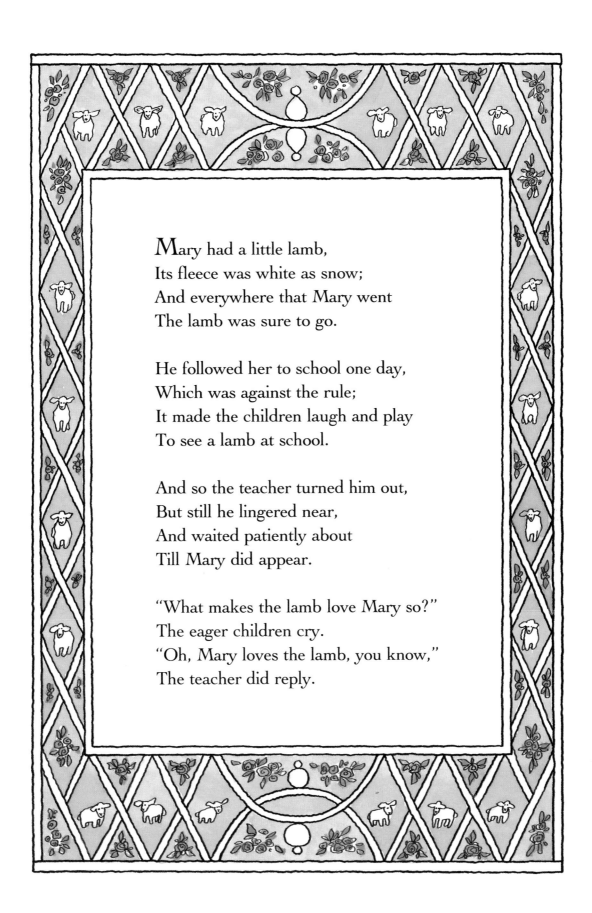

Mary had a little lamb,
Its fleece was white as snow;
And everywhere that Mary went
The lamb was sure to go.

He followed her to school one day,
Which was against the rule;
It made the children laugh and play
To see a lamb at school.

And so the teacher turned him out,
But still he lingered near,
And waited patiently about
Till Mary did appear.

"What makes the lamb love Mary so?"
The eager children cry.
"Oh, Mary loves the lamb, you know,"
The teacher did reply.

Come hither, little puppy dog.
I'll give you a new collar
If you will learn to read your book
And be a clever scholar.

Thirty days hath September,
April, June, and November.
All the rest have thirty-one,
Excepting February alone,
And that has twenty-eight days clear
And twenty-nine in each leap year.

I know something I won't tell.
Three little mouses in a peanut shell,
One can read and one can write
And one can smoke his daddy's pipe.

Great A, little a,
Bouncing B,
The cat's in the cupboard
And can't see me.

A diller, a dollar,
A ten o'clock scholar.
What makes you come so soon?
You used to come at ten o'clock,
But now you come at noon.

Leg over leg
As the dog went to Dover.
When he came to a stile
Jump! he went over.

I do not like thee, Doctor Fell.
The reason why I cannot tell.
But this I know, and know full well:
I do not like thee, Doctor Fell.

Tom, Tom, the piper's son,
Stole a pig and away he run.
The pig was eat and Tom was beat
And Tom went crying down the street.

To market, to market
To buy a fat pig.
Home again, home again
Jiggety-jig.
To market, to market
To buy a fat hog.
Home again, home again
Jiggety-jog.

Peter White will ne'er go right.
Would you know the reason why?
He follows his nose wherever he goes,
And that stands all awry.

Hark, hark, the dogs do bark,
The beggars are coming to town.
Some in rags and some in tags
And some in velvet gowns.

Trit trot to market to buy a penny doll,
Trit trot back again, the market's sold them all.

Hie to the market, Jenny come trot,
Spilt all her buttermilk, every drop,
Every drop and every dram.
Jenny came home with an empty can.

If I'd as much money as I could spend
I never would cry, Old chairs to mend.
Old chairs to mend, old chairs to mend,
I never would cry, Old chairs to mend.

A robin and a robin's son
Once went to town to buy a bun.
They couldn't decide on plum or plain
And so they went back home again.

Mistress Mary
Quite contrary,
How does your garden grow?
With silver bells
And cockleshells
And pretty maids all in a row.

Smiling girls, rosy boys,
Come and buy my little toys:
Monkeys made of gingerbread
And sugar horses painted red.

Green cheese, yellow laces
Up and down the marketplaces.
Turn, cheeses, turn.

Donkey, donkey, do not bray.
Mend your pace and trot away.
Indeed, the market's almost done.
My butter's melting in the sun.

Pussicat, wussicat, with a white foot,
When is your wedding and I'll come to it.
The beer's to brew, the bread's to bake.
Pussicat, wussicat, don't be too late.

Hay is for horses,
Straw is for cows.
Milk is for little pigs
And wash for old sows.

Fiddle-de-dee, fiddle-de-dee,
The fly shall marry the humble-bee.
They went to church and married was she.
The fly has married the humble-bee.

We're all jolly boys,
And we're coming with a noise.
Our coats shall be made
With fine lace brocade.
Our stockings shall be silk
As white as the milk,
And our tails shall touch the ground.

Little Miss Lily, you're dreadfully silly
To wear such a very long skirt.
If you take my advice, you would hold it up nice
And not let it trail in the dirt.

Bless you, bless you, burnie-bee,
Tell me when my wedding be.
If it be tomorrow day
Take your wings and fly away:
Fly to the east, fly to the west,
Fly to him I love the best.

Oh, rare Harry Parry,
When will you marry?

When apples and pears are ripe.

I'll come to your wedding
Without any bidding
And dance and sing all the night.

Sing jigmijole, the pudding bowl,
The table and the frame.
My master he did cudgel me
For kissing of my dame.

One for the money
Two for the show
Three to get ready
And four to go.

I had a little husband
No bigger than my thumb.
I put him in a pint pot
And there I bid him drum.
I bought a little horse
That galloped up and down.
I bridled him and saddled him
And sent him out of town.
I gave him a pair of garters
To garter up his hose
And a little silk handkerchief
To wipe his pretty nose.

First in a carriage
Second in a gig
Third on a donkey
And fourth on a pig.

Alas! alas! for Miss Mackay,
Her knives and forks have run away,
And when the cups and spoons are going
She's sure there is no way of knowing.

Did you see my wife,
Did you see, did you see?
Did you see my wife
Looking for me?
She wears a straw bonnet
With white ribbons on it
And dimity petticoats
Over her knee.

Pussycat ate the dumplings.
Pussycat ate the dumplings.
Mamma stood by and cried, Oh fie!
Why did you eat the dumplings?

Round about the rosebush,
Three steps, four steps.
All the little boys and girls
Are sitting on the doorsteps.

Georgie Porgie, pudding and pie,
Kissed the girls and made them cry.
When the boys came out to play
Georgie Porgie ran away.

Sing a song of sixpence,
A pocket full of rye,
Four-and-twenty blackbirds
Baked in a pie.
When the pie was opened
The birds began to sing.
Was not that a dainty dish
To set before the king?
The king was in his counting house
Counting out his money.
The queen was in the parlor
Eating bread and honey.
The maid was in the garden
Hanging out the clothes.
There came a little blackbird
And pecked off her nose.

I asked my mother for fifteen cents
To see the elephant jump the fence.
He jumped so high that he touched the sky
And never came back till the Fourth of July.

Ladybird, ladybird,
Fly away home.
Your house is on fire
And your children all gone.
All except one,
And that's little Ann,
And she has crept under
The warming pan.

Two little dogs
Sat by the fire
Over a fender of coal dust.
Said one little dog
To the other little dog,
If you won't talk, why I must.

There was a crooked man, and he walked a crooked mile.
He found a crooked sixpence against a crooked stile.
He bought a crooked cat, which caught a crooked mouse,
And they all lived together in a little crooked house.

Little Polly Flinders
Sat among the cinders
Warming her pretty little toes.
Her mother came and caught her
And whipped her little daughter
For spoiling her nice new clothes.

Three wise men of Gotham
Went to sea in a bowl.
If the bowl had been stronger
My song had been longer.

Bow wow wow,
Whose dog art thou?
Little Tom Tinker's dog,
Bow wow wow.

Cobbler, cobbler, mend my shoe,
Get it done by half past two.
Stitch it up and stitch it down,
Then I'll give you half a crown.

Bye baby bunting,
Daddy's gone a-hunting,
To fetch a little rabbit skin
To wrap his baby bunting in.

I had a dog whose name was Buff,
I sent him for a bag of snuff.
He broke the bag and spilt the snuff,
And that was all my penny's worth.

If wishes were horses
Beggars would ride.
If turnips were watches
I would wear one by my side.

Three blind mice, three blind mice,
See how they run, see how they run.
They all ran after the farmer's wife,
Who cut off their tails with a carving knife.
Did you ever see such a sight in your life
As three blind mice?

Rockabye baby, on the treetop,
When the wind blows the cradle will rock.
When the bough breaks the cradle will fall,
And down will come baby, cradle and all.

Old Mother Shuttle
Lived in a coal scuttle
Along with her dog and her cat.
What they ate I can't tell,
But 'tis known very well
That not one of the party was fat.

Seesaw, Margery Daw,
Jack shall have a new master.
He shall have but a penny a day
Because he can't work any faster.

The giant Jim, great giant grim,
Wears a hat without a brim,
Weighs a ton and wears a blouse
And trembles when he meets a mouse.

There was an old woman who lived in a shoe.
She had so many children she didn't know what to do.
She gave them some broth without any bread,
She whipped them all soundly and sent them to bed.

I'll tell my own daddy, when he comes home,
What little good work my mammy has done.
She has earned a penny and spent a groat
And burnt a hole in the child's new coat.

Bell horses, bell horses,
What time o' day?
One o'clock, two o'clock,
Time to away.

Seesaw, sacradown,
Which is the way to Boston town?
One foot up and the other foot down,
That is the way to Boston town.

Ring around a rosey,
A pocket full of posies.
Ashes, ashes,
We all fall down.

Gee up, Neddy, to the fair.
What shall we buy when we get there?
A penny apple and a penny pear.
Gee up, Neddy, to the fair.

See, see, what shall I see?
A horse's head where his tail should be.

Richard Dick upon a stick,
Samson on a sow,
We'll ride away to Colley Fair
To buy a horse to plough.

Simple Simon met a pieman
Going to the fair.
Says Simple Simon to the pieman,
Let me taste your ware.

Says the pieman to Simple Simon,
Show me first your penny.
Says Simple Simon to the pieman,
Indeed I have not any.

If I had a donkey that wouldn't go,
Would I beat him? Oh, no, no.
I'd put him in the barn
And give him some corn,
The best little donkey
That ever was born.

Ride a cockhorse to Banbury Cross
To see an old woman upon a black horse:
A ring on her finger, a bonnet of straw,
The strangest old woman that ever you saw.

As I was going to Newbury
Upon a summer's day,
My dame had butter, eggs, and fruit,
And I had corn and hay.
Joe drove the ox and Tom the swine,
Dick took the foal and mare.
I sold them all, then home to dine
From famous Newbury Fair.

Rub-a-dub-dub,
Three men in a tub,
And who do you think they were?
The butcher, the baker,
The candlestick maker.
They all jumped out of a rotten potato,
'Twas enough to make a man stare.

Hickory dickory dock,
The mouse ran up the clock.
The clock struck one,
The mouse ran down.
Hickory dickory dock.

Goosey goosey gander,
Whither shall I wander?
Upstairs and downstairs
And in my lady's chamber.
There I met an old man
Who would not say his prayers.
I took him by the left leg
And threw him down the stairs.

Hippity-hop to the barber shop
To get a stick of candy.
One for you and one for me
And one for sister Mandy.

Tickly, tickly, on your knee,
If you laugh you don't love me.

Shoe a little horse,
Shoe a little mare,
But let the little colt
Go bare, bare, bare.

When the clouds
Are upon the hills,
They'll come down
By the mills.

Millery millery dustipole,
How many sacks have you stole?
Four-and-twenty and a peck.
Hang the miller by his neck.

It's raining, it's raining,
There's pepper in the box,
And all the little ladies
Are picking up their frocks.

Doctor Foster went to Gloucester
In a shower of rain.
He stepped in a puddle
Right up to his middle
And never went there again.

I had a little moppet,
I kept her in my pocket
And fed her on corn and hay.
There came a proud beggar
And said he would wed her
And stole my little moppet away.

As I was going up Pippen Hill
Pippen Hill was dirty.
There I met a pretty miss
And she dropped me a curtsy.
Little miss, pretty miss,
Blessings light upon you,
If I had half a crown a day
I'd spend it all upon you.

Charley, Charley
Stole the barley
Out of the baker's shop.
The baker came out
And gave him a clout,
Which made poor Charley hop.

Little Boy Blue, come blow your horn,
The sheep's in the meadow, the cow's in the corn.
But where is the little boy tending the sheep?
He's under the haycock fast asleep.
Will you wake him? No, not I,
For if I do he's sure to cry.

Dingty diddlety,
My mammy's maid,
She stole oranges
I am afraid.
Some in her pocket,
Some in her sleeve.
She stole oranges
I do believe.

Cackle cackle, Mother Goose,
Have you any feathers loose?
Truly have I, pretty fellow,
Half enough to fill a pillow.
Here are quills, take one or two,
And down to make a bed for you.

Sally go round the sun,
Sally go round the moon,
Sally go round the chimney pots
On a Saturday afternoon.

Diddlety diddlety dumpty,
The cat ran up the plum tree.
Half a crown to fetch her down,
Diddlety diddlety dumpty.

Tiddle liddle lightum,
Pitch and tar.
Tiddle liddle lightum —
What's that for?

Little Miss Donnet,
She wears a big bonnet
And hoops half as wide
As the mouth of the Clyde.

Charley Barley, butter and eggs,
Sold his wife for three duck eggs.
When the ducks began to lay
Charley Barley flew away.

There was a bee
Sat on a wall.
He said he could hum
And that was all.

Catch him, crow!
Carry him, kite!
Take him away till the apples are ripe.
When they are ripe
And ready to fall,
Here comes baby, apples and all.

Baa, baa, black sheep,
Have you any wool?
Yes sir, yes sir,
Three bags full:
One for my master
And one for my dame
And one for the little boy
That lives in the lane.

A man went hunting at Ryegate
And wished to leap over a high gate.
Says the owner, Go round
With your gun and your hound,
For you never shall leap over my gate.

Wine and cakes for gentlemen,
Hay and corn for horses,
A cup of ale for good old wives,
And kisses for young lasses.

There was an old woman
Lived under a hill,
And if she's not gone
She lives there still.

Baked apples she sold
And cranberry pies,
And she's the old woman
That never told lies.

Peter, Peter, pumpkin eater
Had a wife and couldn't keep her.
He put her in a pumpkin shell
And there he kept her very well.

Peter, Peter, pumpkin eater
Had another and didn't love her.
Peter learned to read and spell
And then he loved her very well.

In the greenhouse lives a wren,
Little friend of little men.
When they're good she tells them where
To find the apple, quince, and pear.

Bring Daddy home
With a fiddle and a drum
A pocket full of spices
An apple and a plum.

Wash the dishes, wipe the dishes,
Ring the bell for tea.
Three good wishes, three good kisses
I will give to thee.

Little Poll Parrot
Sat in his garret
Eating toast and tea.
A little brown mouse
Jumped into the house
And stole it all away.

Sing, sing, what shall I sing?
The cat's run away with the pudding string.
Do, do, what shall I do?
The cat's run away with the pudding too.

Ding dong bell,
Pussy's in the well.
Who put her in?
Little Johnny Green.
Who pulled her out?
Little Tommy Stout.
What a naughty boy was that
To try to drown poor pussycat,
Who never did him any harm
And killed the mice in his father's barn.

104

Hannah Bantry in the pantry
Gnawing on a mutton bone.
How she gnawed it
How she clawed it
When she found herself alone.

Hushabye baby, they're gone to milk.
Lady and milkmaid all in silk.
Lady goes softly, maid goes slow,
Round again, round again, round they go.

Here am I,
Little jumping Joan.
When nobody's with me
I'm always alone.

Polly put the kettle on,
Polly put the kettle on,
Polly put the kettle on,
We'll all have tea.

Sukey take it off again,
Sukey take it off again,
Sukey take it off again,
They've all gone away.

Rumpty-iddity, row row row,
If I had a good supper,
I could eat it now.

Snow, snow faster,
Ally ally blaster.
The old woman's plucking her geese,
Selling the feathers a penny apiece.

Hush thee my babby,
Lie still with thy daddy.
Thy mammy has gone to the mill
To grind thee some wheat
To make thee some meat,
So hushabye, babby, lie still.

Here's Sulky Sue.
What shall we do?
Turn her face to the wall
Till she comes to.

A little old man of Derby,
How do you think he served me?
He took away my bread and cheese
And that is how he served me!

Lucy Locket lost her pocket,
Kitty Fisher found it.
Not a penny was there in it,
Only ribbon round it.

Oh that I were
Where I would be,
Then would I be
Where I am not.
But where I am
There I must be,
And where I would be
I cannot.

Crosspatch,
Draw the latch,
Sit by the fire and spin.
Take a cup
And drink it up,
Then call the neighbors in.

Three little kittens
They lost their mittens
And they began to cry,
Oh mother dear
We sadly fear
Our mittens we have lost.
What? Lost your mittens?
You naughty kittens!
Then you shall have no pie.
Meow meow meow.
No, you shall have no pie.

The north wind doth blow,
And we shall have snow,
And what will poor Robin do then?
Poor thing.
He'll sit in a barn
And keep himself warm
And hide his head under his wing,
Poor thing.

Jeremiah Obadiah, puff, puff, puff,
When he gives his messages he snuffs, snuffs, snuffs.

I had two pigeons bright and gay,
They flew from me the other day.
What was the reason they did go?
I cannot tell for I do not know.

Little Bo-Peep has lost her sheep
And can't tell where to find them.
Leave them alone and they'll come home
Dragging their tails behind them.

Red sky at night,
Sailor's delight.
Red sky in the morning,
Sailors take warning.

My father died a month ago
And left me all his riches:
A feather bed, a wooden leg,
A pair of leather breeches,
A coffee pot without a spout,
A cup without a handle,
A tobacco pipe without a lid,
And half a farthing candle.

P-U-N-kin
N-kin-Y
Double-E-N-kin
Pumpkin Pie.

St. Thomas's Day is past and gone,
And Christmas is a'most a-come.
Maidens arise and make your pies
And save poor tailor Bobby one.

Round about, round about,
Applety pie,
My father loves good ale
And so do I.

Star light, star bright,
First star I've seen tonight.
I wish I may, I wish I might
Have the wish I wish tonight.

Manners in the dining room,
Manners in the hall.
If you don't behave yourself,
You shan't have none at all.

Said Noble Aaron to Aaron Barron,
Oh dear, my foot you put your chair on.
Said Aaron Barron to Noble Aaron,
Oh! you shall put your foot my chair on.

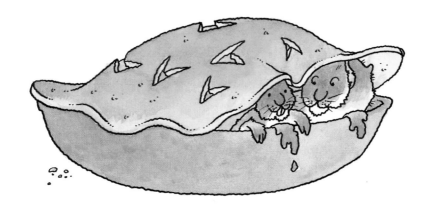

Baby and I
Were baked in a pie,
The gravy was wonderful hot.
We had nothing to pay
To the baker that day,
And so we crept out of the pot.

Tinkle, twinkle, little star,
How I wonder what you are.
Up above the world so high
Like a diamond in the sky,
Twinkle, twinkle, little star,
How I wonder what you are.

Little Tommy Tucker
Sings for his supper.
What shall we give him?
White bread and butter.
How shall he cut it
Without e'er a knife?
How shall he marry
Without e'er a wife?

The fiddler and his wife
The piper and his mother
Ate three half cakes, three whole cakes,
And three-quarters of another.

Jack Sprat could eat no fat,
His wife could eat no lean,
And so betwixt them both, you see,
They licked the platter clean.

Willful waste brings woeful want,
And you may live to say:
How I wish I had that crust
That once I threw away!

Christmas is coming,
The geese are getting fat.
Please to put a penny
In an old man's hat.

The man in the moon
Came down too soon
And asked his way to Norwich.
He went by the south
And burnt his mouth
With supping cold plum porridge.

Wee Willie Winkie runs through the town,
Upstairs and downstairs in his nightgown,
Rapping at the windows, crying at the locks,
Are the children in their beds? For now it's eight o'clock.

Cold and raw the north winds blow
Bleak in the morning early.
All the hills are covered with snow,
And winter's now come fairly.

On Christmas Eve I turned the spit.
I burnt my fingers, I feel it yet.
The little cock sparrow flew over the table,
The pot began to play with the ladle.

John, come sell thy fiddle
And buy thy wife a gown.
No, I'll not sell my fiddle
For ne'er a wife in town.

Hey diddle diddle,
The cat and the fiddle,
The cow jumped over the moon.
The little dog laughed
To see such sport,
And the dish ran away with the spoon.

Old King Cole was a merry old soul
And a merry old soul was he.
He called for his pipe
And he called for his bowl
And he called for his fiddlers three.

Christmas comes but once a year,
And when it comes it brings good cheer —
A pocketful of money and a cellar full of beer
And a good fat pig to last you all the year.

Left foot, right foot,
Any foot at all,
Sally lost her petticoat
A-goin' to the ball.

130

Cock-a-doodle-doo
My dame has lost her shoe.
My master's lost his fiddling stick
And doesn't know what to do.

Cock-a-doodle-doo
What is my dame to do?
Till master finds his fiddling stick
She'll dance without her shoe.

Little Jack Horner
Sat in the corner
Eating his Christmas pie.
He put in his thumb
And pulled out a plum
And said, What a good boy am I!

Who comes here?
  A grenadier.
What do you want?
  A pot of beer.
Where is your money?
  I've forgot.
Get you gone
You drunken sot.

On Saturday night I lost my wife,
And where do you think I found her?
Up in the moon, singing a tune,
And all the stars around her.

Hey ho, nobody home.
Meat nor drink nor money have I none,
Yet will I be merry, merry, merry.
Hey ho, nobody home.

My little old man and I fell out.
How shall we bring this matter about?
Bring it about as well as you can
And get you gone, you little old man.

The moon shines bright,
The stars give a light,
And little Nanny Button-Cap
Will come tomorrow night.

I saw three ships come sailing by,
Come sailing by, come sailing by.
I saw three ships come sailing by
On New Year's Day in the morning.

Come dance a jig
To my granny's pig,
With a randy, rowdy, dowdy.
Come dance a jig
To my granny's pig
And pussycat shall crowdy.

To bed, to bed
Says Sleepyhead.
Let's tarry awhile
Says Slow.
Put on the pot
Says Greedy Sot,
We'll sup before we go.

Here's to thee, old apple tree!
Whence thou mayest bud
And whence thou mayest blow
And whence thou mayest bear
Apples enow,
Hats full and caps full,
Bushels full and sacks full,
And our pockets full too.

God be here, God be there,
We wish you all a happy year.
God without, God within,
Let the Old Year out
And the New Year in.

Rowsty dowt,
My fire is out,
My little maid's not at home!
I'll saddle my cock
And bridle my hen
And fetch my little maid home.

The cat sat asleep by the side of the fire,
The mistress snored loud as a pig.
Jack took up his fiddle by Jenny's desire
And struck up a bit of a jig.

On Friday night I go backwards to bed.
I sleep with my petticoat under my head
To dream of the living and not of the dead,
To dream of the man that I am to wed.

To sleep easy all night
Let your supper be light,
Or else you'll complain
Of a stomach in pain.

Jack be nimble, Jack be quick,
Jack jump over the candlestick.

Go to bed late,
Stay very small.
Go to bed early,
Grow very tall.

Diddle diddle dumpling, my son John
Went to bed with his stockings on.
One shoe off and one shoe on,
Diddle diddle dumpling, my son John.

Little Nancy Etticoat
In a white petticoat
And a red nose —
The longer she stands,
The shorter she grows.

Up the wooden hill to Bedfordshire,
Down Sheet Lane to Blanket Fair.

Good night, sweet repose,
Half the bed and all the clothes.

Go to bed, Tom.
Go to bed, Tom.
Tired or not, Tom—
GO TO BED, TOM!

Higher than a house,
Higher than a tree.
Oh, whatever can that be?

Oh my pretty cock, oh my handsome cock,
I pray you do not crow before day,
And your comb shall be made of the very beaten gold
And your wings of the silver so gray.

We're all dry with drinking on't,
We're all dry with drinking on't.
The piper kissed the fiddler's wife,
And I can't sleep for thinking on't.

Bibliography

Baring-Gould, William S. and Ceil. *The Annotated Mother Goose*. New York: Bramhall House (a division of Clarkson N. Potter), 1962. Includes 883 poems with notes and bibliography.

de Angeli, Marguerite. *Marguerite de Angeli's Book of Nursery and Mother Goose Rhymes*. New York: Doubleday and Company, 1953, 1954.

Grover, Eulalie Osgood. *Mother Goose, The Classic Volland Edition*. Chicago: Rand McNally and Company, 1915.

Opie, Iona and Peter. *The Oxford Dictionary of Nursery Rhymes*. Oxford: Oxford University Press, 1951. Includes 551 poems with notes.

———. *The Oxford Nursery Rhyme Book*. Oxford: Oxford University Press, 1955. Includes 800 poems with bibliography.

The Real Mother Goose. Chicago: Rand McNally and Company, 1916.

Wood, Ray. *The American Mother Goose*. New York: Frederick A. Stokes Company, 1940.

Index of First Lines

Subject Index

155

There was an old man
And he had a calf,
And that's half.
He took him out of the stall
And put him on the wall,
And that's all.

E 398.8 WATSON

DATE DUE

Wendy Watson's
Mother Goose

SEP 3 0 '94	AUG 9 2000		
OCT 2 6 '94	JUN 2 8 2000		
AUG 8 '95	JUL 1 3 2001		
NOV 2 6 1996	JUL 2 7 2001		
DEC 2 1 1996	JUN 2 8 2003		
JAN 3 1 1997	JUL 2 8 2004		
APR 9 1997	AUG 3 0 2004		
JAN 2 0 1998	JUL 1 2 2005		
JUL 1 3 1998	JUL 2 2 2004		
SEP 8 1998	OCT 1 4 2003		
JUL 6 1999	FEB 2 8 2004		
AUG 6 1999	MAY 8 2004		
JUL 5 2000			

GAYLORD   PRINTED IN U.S.A.